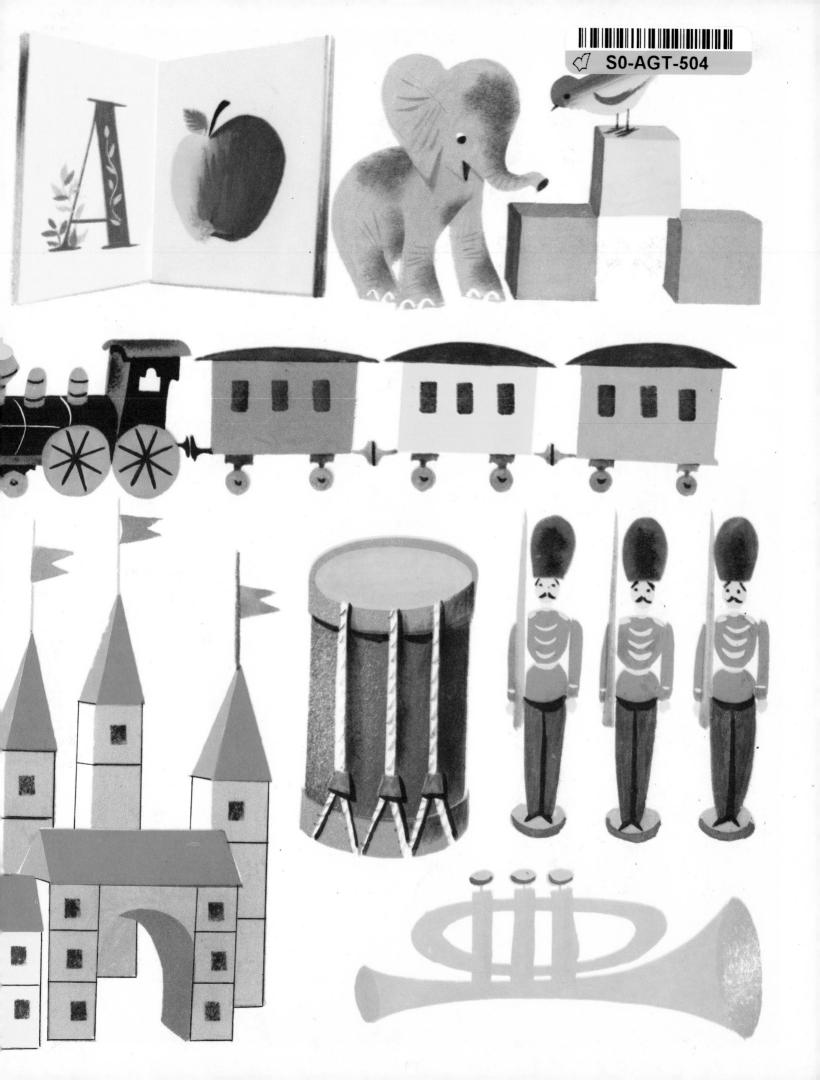

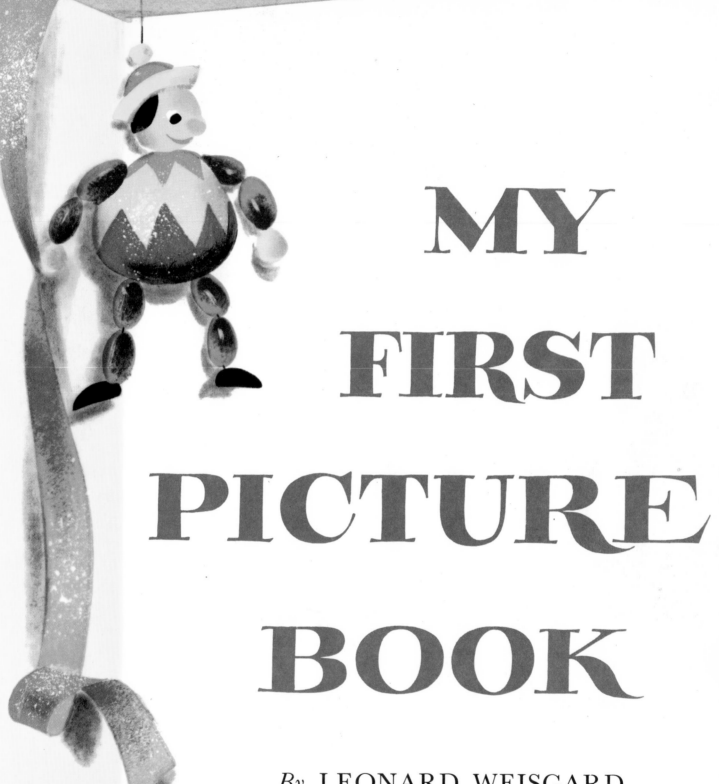

MY
FIRST
PICTURE
BOOK

By LEONARD WEISGARD

GROSSET & DUNLAP *Publishers* NEW YORK

This is my

PICTURE

BOOK

JOHN PAUL

FROM
Sarah

ISBN: 0-448-04246-0
Copyright © 1953, 1981 by Rudolph J. Gutmann.
All rights reserved. Printed in the United States of America.
Published simultaneously in Canada.

1982 PRINTING

All around the kitchen, what do you see?

I see something big made of wood.
I see some little furry animals.
I see something hot.
I see something round to eat on.
Run, run, run, little mice. I see a playful kitten!

All about the school, what do you see?

I see something feathery and funny.
I see a schoolhouse.
I see something to read.
I see something round and good to eat.
I see four little girls.
I see six little boys.
Dance, dance, dance all around the Maypole!

All around the toy box, what do you see?

I see something all dressed up.
I see something big and wooden.
I see a wooden doll.
I see lots of animals all in a row.
Fun, fun, fun, let's have fun with toys!

All about a stage show, what do you see?

I see something on the stage.
I see lots of scenery.
I see something standing on its hind legs.
I see three dogs.
I see something funny wearing a hat.
Laugh, laugh, laugh at the funny show.

All about the woods, what do you see?

I see something swimming.
I see something flying.
I see many pretty flowers.
I see lots of little animals.
Skip, skip, skip away, here comes a baby skunk!

All around the play room, what do you see?

I see something with paint on it.
I see three paint brushes.
I see lots of things in a picture. Look at all the colors.
I see somebody looking at the picture.
Paint, paint, paint, let's paint a picture.

All around the country, what do you see?

I see something moving fast.
I see a big bridge.
I see something small and yellow.
I see a railroad station.
Chug, chug, chug, I see two little dogs going to the country.

All under the sea, what do you see?

I see something heavy tied to a piece of rope.
I see something crawling.
I see something broken.
I see something swimming.
Splash, splash, splash, let's make waves in the sea.

All about the circus, what do you see?

I see something all dressed up in a funny costume.
I see something big and gray.
I see something in a cage.
I see something wearing a hat.
Look, look, look, there's so much to see at the circus!

All around the farm, what do you see?

I see a big red barn.
I see something that says neigh, neigh.
I see something that says oink, oink, oink.
I see something that says cluck, cluck, cluck.
Giddap, giddap, giddap, look at the horse and wagon.

All around the mail box, what do you see?

I see a red flag.
I see something flying by.
I see something in an envelope.
I see something furry and cute.
Surprise, surprise, surprise, I hope there is a
surprise for me!

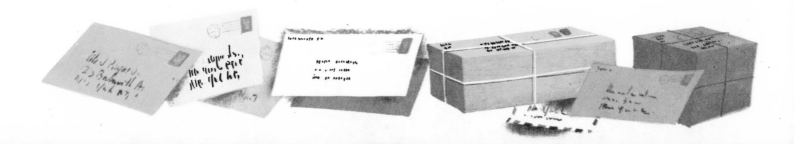

All about make-believe magic, what do you see?

I see something wearing a hat.
I see something in a mirror.
I see something hiding.
I see a broken egg shell.
Hocus pocus, let's pretend this is a magic rabbit.

All around the harbor, what do you see?

I see something in a boat.
I see something tall with a torch in her hand.
I see something flying.
Toot, toot, toot, let's sail around the harbor
and watch the big boats.

All around the pet shop, what do you see?

I see something brown and soft and woolly.
I see something that can talk. It has a long tail.
I see something with blue eyes.
I see lots of furry animals in little cages.
Bark, bark, bark, let's have fun in the pet shop!

All around the zoo, what do you see?

I see something blue.
I see something in a cage.
I see something very furry.
I see something with a great big beak.
I see something on a string.
Peek, peek, peek, I see you at the zoo.

All about a fire, what do you see and hear?

I see a big empty building.
I hear something crackling.
I hear something clanging.
I see things that keep the yard clean.
Clang-a-lang-a-lang, here come the engines
to put the fire out.

All about animal sounds, what do you see?

I see something playing the harp.
I see something playing the drums.
I see something holding a violin.
I see something playing a French horn.
Tweet, tweet, tweet, let's sing like the birds!

All about the little park, what do you see?

I see something sitting in a tree.
I see people standing on the ground.
I see something floating on the lake.
I see something round on strings.
Blow, wind, blow, and the boats will go.

All around the town, what do you see?

I see something that can turn red and green.
I see a policeman riding a horse.
I see a wagon with something in it.
I see two soft and furry animals.
Honk, honk, honk, now it's time to let the cars go by.

All around the garden, what do you see?

I see something jumping.
I see something munching.
I see something wooden.
I see good things to eat.
Sniff, sniff, sniff, smell the pretty roses.

All about the backyard, what do you see and hear?

I see lots of things flapping in the wind.
I hear something meowing.
I see a wooden fence.
I see many buildings.
Tap, tap, tap, listen to the wind on the window pane.

All about the nursery, what do you see?

I see something that rocks.
I see something that goes "boom, boom."
I see a house built of blocks.
I see something alive.
March, march, march, soldiers can march.

MY
FIRST
PICTURE
BOOK